JESUS
Our Treasure

A MUSICAL DRAMA FOR CHRISTMAS

CREATED BY
MIKE HARLAND

ARRANGED AND ORCHESTRATED BY
CAMP KIRKLAND

SCRIPT BY
LAWRENCE KIMBROUGH

PRODUCTS AVAILABLE

Choral Book..1-4158-2250-6

Listening CD*.......................................1-4158-2251-4

Accompaniment CD...........................1-4158-2248-4
(split track only)

Orchestration 1-4158-2249-2

Rehearsal Tracks CD.........................1-4158-2244-1

Posters (Pack of 10)..........................1-4158-2246-8

Bulletins (Pack of 100).......................1-4158-2245-X

CD Promo Pak.....................................1-4158-2247-6

*Listening CDs are available at a reduced rate when bought
in quantities of 10 or more.

Scripture quotations are taken from the Holman Christian Standard Bible®, Copyright © 1999, 2000, 2002, 2003
by Holman Bible Publishers. Used by permission. Holman Christian Standard Bible®, Holman CSB®,
and HCSB® are federally registered trademarks of Holman Bible Publishers.

GENEVOX
1-4158-2250-6

INSTRUMENTATION

Let There Be Joy with *Joy to the World! The Lord Is Come* and *How Great Our Joy*
Glory to God
My Son, My Lord with *What Child Is This**
Go, Tell Everybody with *Go, Tell It on the Mountain*
Herod's Song
Jesus, Our Treasure
Who Am I?
What Can I Give Him? with *Everything***
Jesus, What a Wonder You Are with *Fairest Lord Jesus*
Finale includes *Go, Tell Everybody* with *Go, Tell It on the Mountain*
and *Jesus, Our Treasure*

INSTRUMENTATION: Flute 1-2, Oboe, Clarinet 1-2, Bassoon, Bass Clarinet, Trumpet 1, Trumpet 2-3, Horn 1-2, Trombone 1-2, Trombone 3/Tuba, Percussion 1-2, Drum Set, Harp, Rhythm, Violin 1-2, Viola, Cello, String Bass

SUBSTITUTE PARTS: Alto Sax 1-2 (substitute for French Horn), Tenor Sax/Baritone Treble Clef (substitute for Trombone 1-2), Clarinet 3 (substitute for Viola), Keyboard String Reduction

The rhythm part in this orchestration is designed to provide satisfying accompaniment throughout. However, keyboard players may find it helpful to reference certain passages in the choral score to supply the most supportive accompaniment.

*This selection omits drum set.
**This selection omits trumpets.

---

*Interlude 1****
Interlude 2

INSTRUMENTATION: Flute 1-2, Oboe, Clarinet 1-2, Bassoon, Bass Clarinet, Horn 1-2, Rhythm, Violin 1-2, Viola, Cello, String Bass

SUBSTITUTE PARTS: Clarinet 3 (substitute for Viola), Keyboard String Reduction

The rhythm part in this orchestration is designed to provide satisfying accompaniment throughout. However, keyboard players may find it helpful to reference certain passages in the choral score to supply the most supportive accompaniment.

***This selection omits Horn 1-2.

Interlude 3

INSTRUMENTATION: Horn 1-2, Trombone 1-2, Trombone 3/Tuba

SUBSTITUTE PARTS: Alto Sax 1-2 (substitute for French Horn), Tenor Sax/Baritone Treble Clef (substitute for Trombone 1-2)

The rhythm part in this orchestration is designed to provide satisfying accompaniment throughout. However, keyboard players may find it helpful to reference certain passages in the choral score to supply the most supportive accompaniment.

FOREWORDS

Having worked on numerous Christmas musicals, it is always interesting to hear a new "voice" speak to this wonderful subject. Working with Mike Harland, Lawrence Kimbrough, and the LifeWay Worship Music Group team proved to be exactly that—a new "voice." I believe this musical is a truly "personal" approach to this timeless revealing of God's love for us. The songs are the truth of the message that God would have us hear, focus on, and apply to our lives. Rejoice with us as you sing and play these rich and vital songs.

Camp Kirkland

From Day 1, I loved Mike Harland's idea of looking back at Christmas, not across two yawning millennia, but through the eyes of an old shepherd's still-fresh memories from 40 years before. To me, it is sort of the way we might remember some huge national event from the 60s or 70s, our wedding day in the 80s, perhaps our personal encounter with Christ in the not too distant past. Imagine being able to think back to Christmas with that kind of clarity and context, recalling everything, even down to the minor details that could only be picked up by those who were there, who felt it, who saw it, who lived it.

As you experience this musical in your church and life, I pray that the One to whom a thousand years is still like a day will compress the time for you between this Christmas and that one. I hope He will make its reality resonate within you in ways that comfort and surprise you. And I join you in trusting Him to pour out His Spirit through you as you work, rehearse, fine-tune, and deliver this musical. I know He will.

My thanks to Mike for letting me tinker around and give voice to his characters, to editor in chief, Randy Smith, for the gutsy willingness to trust me with something new, to Camp Kirkland for being there to listen and lead, and to my LifeWay Worship Music Group friends who sweat the details so God's people can sing.

Lawrence Kimbrough

CONTENTS

Let There Be Joy
with
Joy to the World! The Lord Is Come
and
How Great Our Joy

Arranged by Camp Kirkland

6

8

† "How Great Our Joy"

Let there be, let there be praise.____

Add ALTOS

Let there be, let there be joy.____

6 Add SOPRANOS

Let there be, let there be joy.____

* Use cue notes only if needed for range.

16

INTERLUDE 1
Jesus, Our Treasure

Words and Music by MIKE HARLAND,
LUKE GARRETT, and CHRIS MACHEN
Arranged by Camp Kirkland

SCENE 1

Characters: **Miriam**, **Jacob**, and three **shepherds**

Setting: **Miriam** is alone in Jacob's shed but is soon joined by **Jacob**. On a separate part of the stage, **shepherds** are sitting together, tending their sheep.

MIRIAM: *(thinking aloud)* Oh, I love it in here, in my grandfather's shed. Most of the time my big brothers are in and out of here, getting tools and looking for things. But sometimes…sometimes *(looking around to see if anyone is coming)*…if I time it just right, I can poke around in here myself—just to see what I can see…

Like *(looking around, then finding something)*—well, like one of these little wooden sheep my grandfather used to carve before his hands got too stiff and he couldn't make them anymore. *(She tosses it back and forth in her hands, playing with it.)* He gave me one sort of like this once. *(She puts it back where she found it.)*

Or *(looking around again)*—like this old sickle. *(She picks it up by the handle, holding it in front of her, the blade just above eye level.)* I'm not supposed to touch the blade because it's too sharp and everything. *(She gazes long and hard at the sharp blade, nursing the temptation but not giving in.)*…AND because I've already gotten in trouble for it about 20 times *(setting it down, with a little laugh under her breath).*

Or like—oh, I know *(raising her right index finger, remembering something; she kneels down and begins searching for something)*! Like the fancy robe my mother made for him when she was just a girl. Grandfather told her he lost it by accident, but I happen to know that he hides it under here so he never has to…

JACOB: *(while she's still kneeling down, her back to him, searching)* Miriam!

MIRIAM: *(startled, she tries to stand, stumbling to her feet)* Yes, sir? Yes, sir?

JACOB: What are you looking for?

MIRIAM: Oh, I was just, uh…I was just, uh…

JACOB: *(pausing for effect, then speaking slowly, with a knowing smile)* Keeping our little secret?

MIRIAM: *(laughs, relieved)* Yes, sir.

JACOB: Well, your grandmother asked me to come out here and look for you. You haven't been, uh, touching anything, have you?

MIRIAM: Oh, no, sir.

JACOB: Like that sharp sickle?

MIRIAM: No, sir. I promise.

JACOB: *(pausing as he glances toward his shepherd's staff, which is supported by nails so it can hang horizontally on the wall)* Or like my shepherd's staff, for instance *(reaching up to take it from its special place)*?

MIRIAM: No, sir! NO, SIR! I'd never touch that!

JACOB: Well, it's not that I mind you touching it *(admiring it, the memories flooding back)*. I just want to be sure that nothing ever happens to this. Of all the things I own, nothing means more to me than this staff *(continuing to run his fingers along the grain)*—not my land, not my livestock, not even that crazy-colored robe you were looking for a minute ago *(laughs, then becomes serious again)*. No, this staff is my greatest treasure.

MIRIAM: *(drawing close to him, pausing before speaking)* You haven't told me that story in a long time, Grandfather—about the night you were using that staff when the angels came to see you.

JACOB: I guess I haven't, have I? Oh, Miriam, it was UN-BE-LIEVABLE *(lights come up on shepherds)*. We were just sitting there, a couple of other fellows and me—bored, like always—when out of nowhere, this *(music begins)*. . .this "person"…appeared. And light started shining all around us! And then he started talking to us…about our "Savior" being born…even down to where the Boy was and what He was wearing! And all the time, my mouth's hanging open, and my eyes are bugging out. Even the sheep were in shock! And then came MORE angels…and MORE angels…and more…and more…and more!

Glory to God

Words and Music by
MIKE HARLAND and LUKE GARRETT
Arranged by Camp Kirkland

*"...this...this **person** appeared..."*

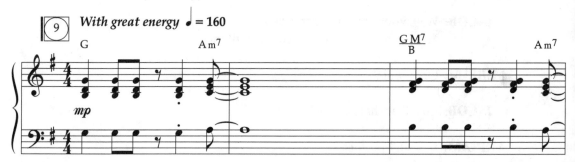

"...shining all around us..."

"...being born. Even down to where the Boy was..."

"...my mouth's hanging open and my eyes..."

"...and then came more angels..."

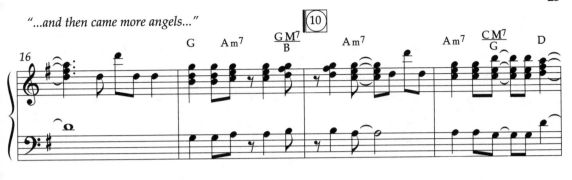

LADIES unis. *(1st time)*
MEN unis. *(2nd time)*

While shep-herds watched_ their flocks_ by night,_ a

(2nd time only)
to the world!_ the Lord_ is come;_ Let

L. H. tacet 1st time

new song filled_ the sky._____ And

earth re - ceive_ her King!_____ If

24

ry   to God   in the   high   -   -   -   -   -

est!_____   MEN unis. *mf*

Joy

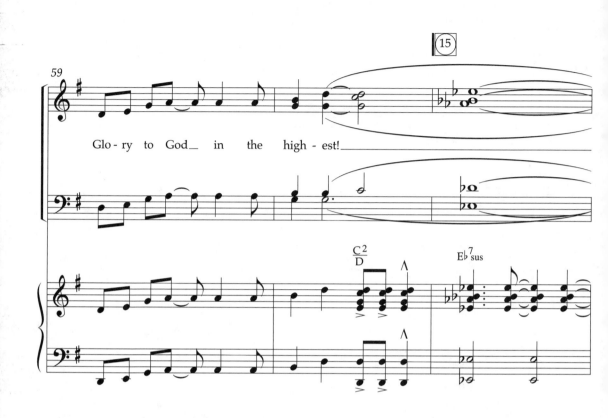

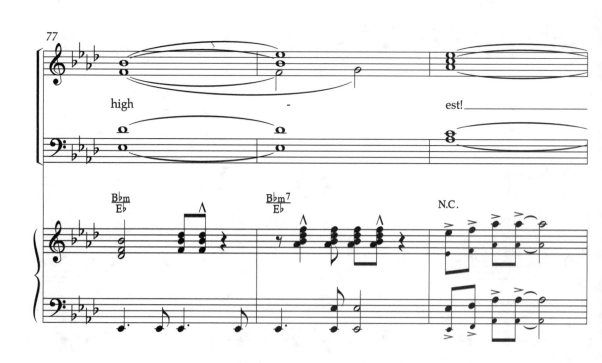

Glo - ry to God___ in the high - est!___

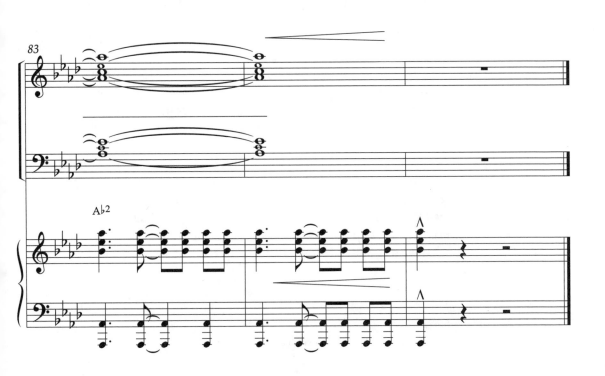

⟶ SCENE 2 ⟶

Characters: **Jacob**, **Miriam**, **shepherds**, **Mary**, **Joseph**, and **Baby Jesus**

Setting: **Jacob** and **Miriam** are still in his shed. He's leaning on his staff; she's standing next to him. The **shepherds** are trying to gather their composure as the angelic light fades and night again descends around them. During **Jacob** and **Miriam's** conversation, the **shepherds** begin moving toward the manger scene, where **Mary** and **Joseph** are caring for their new Baby Son.

JACOB: I've tried every way I know to describe it, Miriam, but *(turning to her)*…have you ever just been scared out of your skin?

MIRIAM: *(thinking a second)* There was one time, I remember, when I got caught in a really bad lightning storm. I had to run and hide, all scrunched down in a cave, until it finally quit.

JACOB: Well…I'm telling you, this was louder than 10 thunderstorms, all hitting at once, spraying us from all sides, with nothing to hide under. We thought we were dead! But worse than that, we thought we might NOT be…and that the angels might come back!

MIRIAM: But if it was so scary, then why—

JACOB: *(interrupting)* I know, I know, it's hard to understand. But sometimes, Miriam, I guess sometimes God has to scare us, or we'd never stop long enough to know that there's more to life than…sheep, and…shearing days, and…supper just before dark.

I mean, how else would a bunch of silly shepherds have ended up flying off into town in the middle of the night—all stubbly and grass-stained— unless we were scared NOT to? If all God ever did was just sit back and wait for us to notice Him, we might never know, we might never see *(pausing, then snapping back from his philosophical moment)*. Anyway, that's what we did—ran into town and kept on running till we finally found where the Baby was.

*(Lights up on the manger scene. **Joseph** rushes to greet the **shepherds,** like any new father would—careful to protect **Mary's** rest and privacy, while also wanting to show off his Baby. He motions for the **shepherds** to stay quiet, yet welcomes them in.)*

His father, Joseph, sorta met us at the door, looking kinda tense and nervous himself. But Mary, the Baby's mother, barely stirred. I'm not even sure she noticed us. She just sat there, holding Him, rocking Him,

SOLO - Mary

Je - sus,— what a won-der You are.— Je - sus,— Heav-en's bright - est Star.— Je - sus,— You have cap-tured my heart.— Je - sus,——— what a won-der You are.—

singing to Him…

MIRIAM: *("My Son, My Lord" begins)* She didn't look scared?

JACOB: You'd think so, wouldn't you? Being in such a strange place, being responsible for such a special Baby. But, somehow, she was able to just treasure the moment. If only you could have seen her, Miriam. I can still hear her singing…

(As **Mary** *begins singing "My Son, My Lord," the* **shepherds** *stop mingling. One at a time they slide to their knees, each reacting differently—one covering his face and fighting back tears, one gazing toward heaven and sighing with wonder, one just beaming at the mother and child. As* **Joseph** *begins singing his solo, the* **shepherds** *pull back, slipping away without a lot of notice or commotion. The scene now belongs to* **Mary**, **Joseph**, *and the* **Baby**.*)*

My Son, My Lord
with
What Child Is This

Words and Music by
MIKE HARLAND and LUKE GARRETT
Arranged by Camp Kirkland

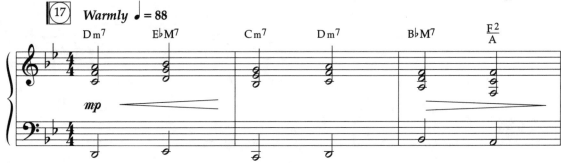

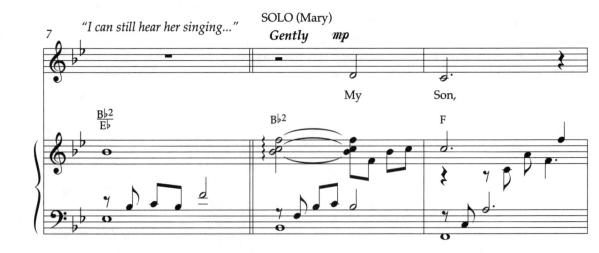

35

36

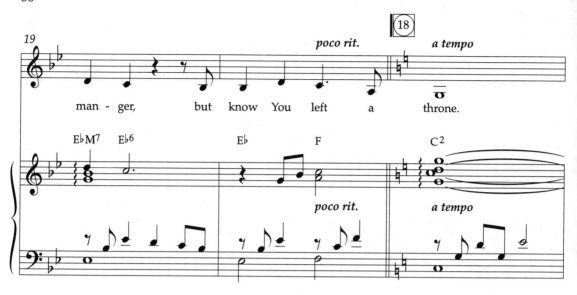

Shep - herd. You are my lit - tle Lamb.

SOLO (Joseph)

My Son, my

Lord, Your life is not from me.

38

40

seem so small and help - less,_____ and

yet You made the world._____

† "What Child Is This." Words by WILLIAM C. DIX. Music Traditional English Melody.

laud,_____ The Babe,_____ the Son_____ of

Ma - ry!

⟋ **SCENE 3** ⟋

Characters: **Shepherds** and crowd

Setting: Although the **shepherds** are carrying the dialogue, the lights are also on **Jacob** as he watches himself reliving the scene from 40 years before. He puts his arm around **Miriam's** shoulder, pointing to the **shepherds** as though he and she can actually see the scene unfolding.

YOUNG JACOB: *(excitedly whispering)* I've got to go tell my family about this! *(beginning to rush off, heading for home)*

SHEPHERD 2: But wait, Jacob, *(stopping him)* no one will believe us!

YOUNG JACOB: BELIEVE us? Look at my face! Look at HIS face! *(popping the cheek of the other* **shepherd***)* Feel what's in your heart *(striking an open palm to the chest of* **shepherd 2***)*! Do I understand it? No. But I dare anyone to look into my eyes and tell me I haven't seen Him. That Baby Boy is our Messiah. This Jesus is going to grow up to become our Deliverer. And He's here, tonight, in Bethlehem! *(music begins)*

Sir, *(quickly stopping a passerby)* have you heard the news? *(The man shakes his head.)* About the new Baby? He was just born in that stable, right over there. He's the Messiah, I tell you! We saw Him with our own eyes! Just tonight, my friends and I were out watching our sheep…*(continue this line of sharing, ad libbing)*

SHEPHERD 3: *(inspired by* **Jacob's** *boldness, he stops another passerby)* Hey, have you heard? The Messiah was born tonight…right here…in Bethlehem. *(continue ad libbing)*

*(While **Jacob** and **Shepherd 3** are witnessing, **Shepherd 2** watches a passerby walk right past him. He is still not sure what to say, but then—after hesitating—he chases the person down from behind and begins a similar "Have you heard?" conversation. He draws the person back toward center stage, where the other **shepherds** are. All three are now talking at once to the gathering crowd, playing off each other's accounts, moving in position to continue their pantomime as the choir sings.)*

Go, Tell Everybody
with
Go, Tell It on the Mountain

Words and Music by
LUKE GARRETT and MIKE HARLAND
Arranged by Camp Kirkland

"Sir, have you heard the news?..."

"He's the Messiah, I tell you..."

"...the Messiah was born tonight..."

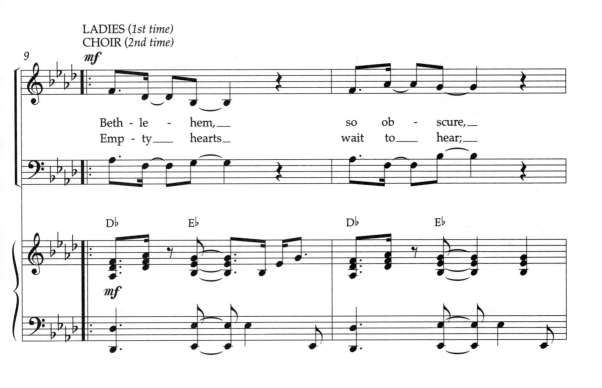

52

54

† "Go, Tell It on the Mountain"

† "Go, Tell It on the Mountain." Words by JOHN W. WORK, JR. Music African-American Spiritual.

56

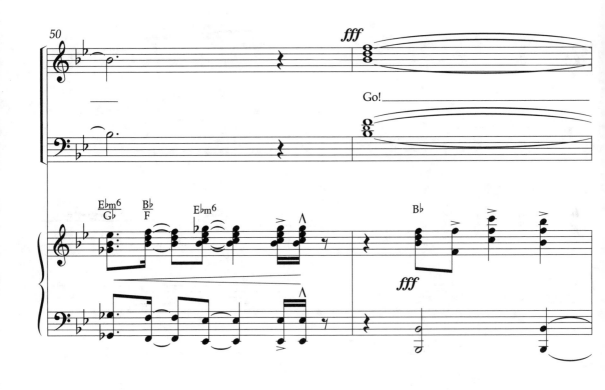

❧ SCENE 4 ❧

Characters: **Jacob**, **Miriam**, and **Herod**

> *Setting:* **Jacob** and **Miriam** are seated on hay bales. The shepherd's staff is leaning against the wall near them. **Herod** is in his court on another part of the stage.

JACOB: If only it could have stayed that way. It was SO exciting that night! Everyone we told was AMAZED at what we were saying! Even the ones who were the most skeptical couldn't help but wonder, "What if it's true? What if this really IS the Savior?"

MIRIAM: But why DIDN'T it stay that way?

JACOB: *(standing, going over to pick up his staff)* Because someone very important was wondering the exact same thing: "What if it's true? What if this IS the Savior…the King of the Jews?"

MIRIAM: Who? Who are you talking about?

JACOB: You know Herod? Herod Antipas?

MIRIAM: Yes.

JACOB: You know how bad he is?

MIRIAM: I've heard you say.

JACOB: Yes, well, many years ago, before he came along, there was another Herod…Herod the Great.

*(Lights up on **Herod**. After giving the audience an adequate arms-folded picture of his power, he begins to pace and look sinister, often turning to look over his shoulder, behind his back.)*

JACOB: *(continuing)* And late in his reign, not long before he died, he got to thinking that everyone was out to get him. You know how it feels, Miriam, when you're fooled by a spooky shadow? Or when you're startled by some animal rustling in the bushes?

MIRIAM: Sure.

JACOB: Well, Herod was old by this time, and all he could see in his head anymore were shadows and darkness. All he could hear were whispers and lies and dirty tricks. He even killed two of his OWN SONS—and was close to killing a third!—thinking they were all plotting against him...before he started to kill every little boy who he thought might be the Messiah, every single boy in sight who was two years old or younger (**Jacob** *pauses, grabbing his staff hard in both hands*)...including...mine.

*(At this, **Herod** spins and glares harshly in **Jacob's** direction. **Jacob** returns the stare, flexing his fists hard around his shepherd's staff...even raising it a little, representative of the many times he'd wished he could use it to bash in the king's head.)*

MIRIAM: *(stunned)* WHAT?! Before he did WHAT?! *(music begins)*

*(lights immediately down on **Jacob** and **Miriam**)*

Herod's Song
(I Am the King)

Words and Music by
MIKE HARLAND and LUKE GARRETT
Arranged by Camp Kirkland

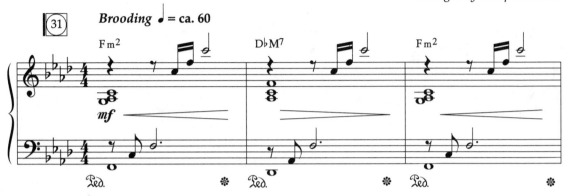

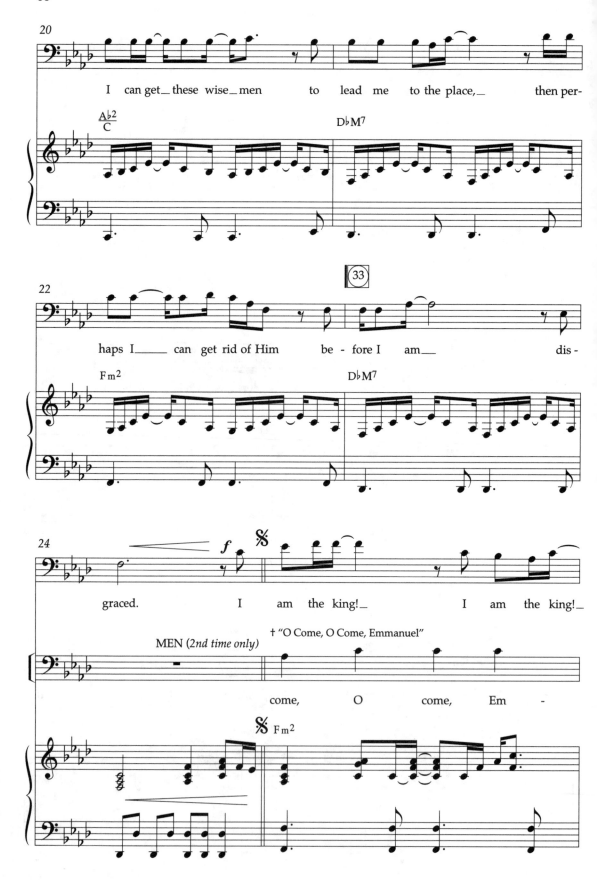

† "O Come, O Come, Emmanuel." Words Latin Hymn, tr. John Mason Neale. Music Plainsong.

2nd time to Coda ⊕
(to meas. 46)

And no lit-tle Boy_ is gon-na come_ to

2nd time to Coda ⊕
(to meas. 46)

man - u - el!

(MEN out)

D♭M⁷   B♭m⁷   A♭2/C   **2nd time to Coda** ⊕
(to meas. 46)

take my crown a - way._____

B♭m⁷

34

I am the king!___

B♭m⁷   Fm²

ti - ny threat is through. If I'm add-ing right, this lit-tle boy could

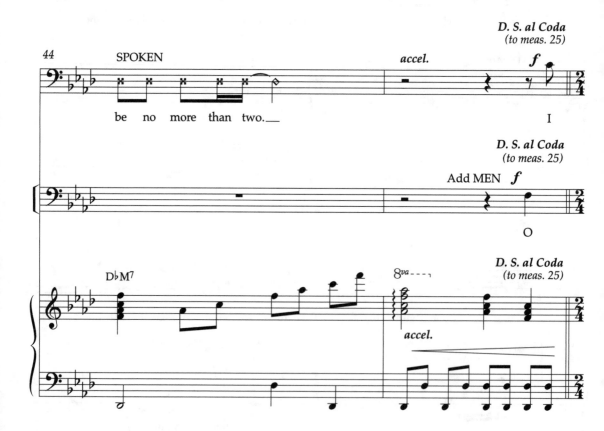

SPOKEN

be no more than two.

D. S. al Coda
(to meas. 25)

I

D. S. al Coda
(to meas. 25)

Add MEN

O

D. S. al Coda
(to meas. 25)

(Segue directly to Interlude 2)

INTERLUDE 2
O Come, O Come, Emmanuel

PLAINSONG, adapt. Thomas Helmore
Arranged by Camp Kirkland

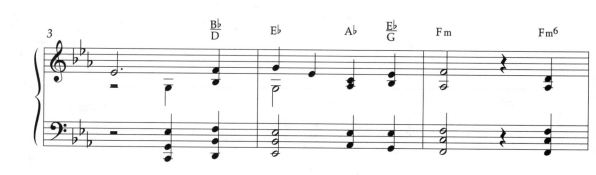

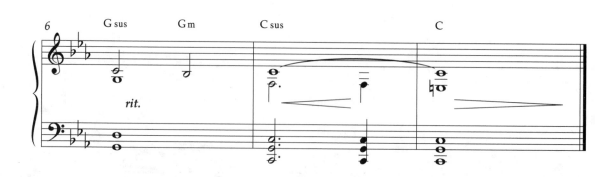

◆ SCENE 5 ◆

Characters: **Jacob**, **Miriam**, three **wise men**, **Mary**, **Joseph**, and **young Jesus**

Setting: **Miriam** has gotten up and run to her grandfather's side, as he continues to gaze into the darkness left by the now-dimmed spotlight on **Herod**. **Mary**, **Joseph**, and **young Jesus** are at their house in Bethlehem.

JACOB: *(gathering himself, a little choke in his voice)* My firstborn son, my little treasure…

MIRIAM: I…I never knew.

JACOB: I know. I know. I probably shouldn't have told you about this, Miriam, but *(appearing sorry at first that he let this slip, then quickly and resolutely determining within himself that he should)*…but you SHOULD know. It's IMPORTANT that you know *(becoming more animated, standing back a little to give himself room to gesture)*. The only way I can tell you what this shepherd's staff means to me is to tell you what it costs—not in money, but in real life. To follow Jesus means giving up things that are very precious to you…even things you never EXPECTED to be precious to you…like anger…like revenge…like self-pity and bitterness and…unforgiveness.

(pausing, then speaking a little more quietly) If it hadn't been for Jesus, I never would have learned that you can give up everything…the good, the bad, the safe, the secure *(looking down at the staff in his hands)*…everything…and still come away with more than you had before.

*(Looking back at **Miriam** after giving this poignant moment a deep breath)* The same thing was true for those wise men from the east I told you about. You remember?

MIRIAM: I sure do.

JACOB: The ones that came to Bethlehem not long after Jesus was born?

MIRIAM: Uh-huh. I love that story.

JACOB: Even with the gifts they brought to Him—gold, frankincense, myrrh—they still returned home with so much more than they came with.

I'm just a poor shepherd, you know. You don't see any gold lying around here, do you? Let me stand a little closer to you. Does that smell like perfume I'm wearing? *(waving his hand in front of an armpit)*

MIRIAM: *(laughing)* Oh, Grandfather…

JACOB: No, the only treasure any of us really have, *(music begins)* whether we're wise men or shepherds, or giggly little grandchildren *(hugging Miriam with one arm)*…our only treasure is Jesus.

*(The **wise men** trail in from the side of the stage, heading for the holy family's house in Bethlehem. As the **wise men** reach **Mary**, **Joseph**, and **young Jesus**, they lay down their gifts, one by one, bowing in worship. They remain throughout the song, singing together, interacting with the family…especially with Jesus…until the music ends and the lights go down.)*

Jesus, Our Treasure

Words and Music by MIKE HARLAND,
LUKE GARRETT, and CHRIS MACHEN
Arranged by Camp Kirkland

76

78

come to wor - ship Je - sus; gifts of praise are what we bring.___ Yet the

CHOIR *mp*

Ooo_____

G² Cm⁶/G

mf

best we have___ to of - fer seems so small be - fore this King. But we'll

TRIO unis.

Ooo_____

G² Cm⁶/G

85

88

INTERLUDE 3
Jesus, Our Treasure

Music by MIKE HARLAND,
LUKE GARRETT, and CHRIS MACHEN
Arranged by Camp Kirkland

～ **SCENE 6** ～

Characters: **Jacob** and **Miriam**

Setting: They are sitting on hay bales in **Jacob's** shed. **Jacob** has his staff.

MIRIAM: *(music begins)* I wish I could have known Him…Jesus, I mean.

JACOB: It was funny, Miriam. You'd hear about Him all the time. Even when He was far away up in Galilee, the stories would trickle down…how He healed the blind and cured the lepers and fed the hungry. *(remembering a personal connection)* Well, you remember old Lazarus over in Bethany?

MIRIAM: Oh, sure, I know about him. Jesus raised him from the dead!

JACOB: Raised him from the dead. Now that was something!

But it was more than just the miracles. It was the way He talked, the answers He gave, the wisdom He had. I remember how He would walk along here and people would holler out to Him, "I'll follow You, Jesus, wherever You go!" And He'd say something about foxes having dens and birds having nests. "'But the Son of Man,'" He said, "'has no place to lay His head'"(Matt. 8:20, Luke 9:58). I'll never forget that.

I've seen Him gather little children—about your age and younger—around Him, and a big smile on His face, laughing like someone had just told Him the funniest joke in the world.

And His stories! He told one about a man walking down that big curvy road that comes through the hills from Jericho.

MIRIAM: Oh, I've heard that one—about the Samaritan who stopped to help the beat-up man even when the priest and the Levite wouldn't do it.

JACOB: He was amazing. I even heard He was out in a boat once with His friends when a big storm blew in from out of nowhere. He just turned His face to the rain and the lightning and said, "Silence!" *(snapping his fingers)* And just like that, everything was calm!

MIRIAM: Wow!

JACOB: Yes.…Wow! *(standing, turning his full attention to the audience while **Miriam** stays seated behind him, still watching him) (music begins)*
And it just makes me think, Why me? Why would God pick a one-in-a-thousand shepherd like me? Why would He come to find me on a… one-in-a-thousand hillside? Why would He send—I don't know—what seemed like a thousand angels…to give me the once-in-a-lifetime—the once-in-ALL-time chance—to see His only Son with my very own eyes before anyone else had seen Him on earth?

Why? I mean…WHO am I? *(begin solo)*

Who Am I?

Words and Music by MARK HALL
Arranged by Camp Kirkland

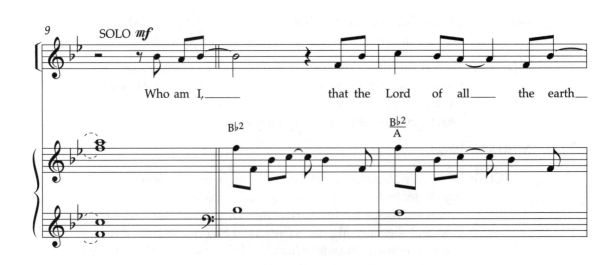

Who am I,_____ that the Lord of all_____ the earth_____

wave tossed__ in the o - cean, a va-por in__ the__ wind.

Still, You hear me when__ I'm call - ing. Lord, You

catch me when__ I'm fall - ing, and You've

day and gone____ to-mor - row, a wave tossed__ in the o-

cean, a va - por in___ the__ wind. Still, You

hear me when__ I'm call - ing. Lord, You catch me when__ I'm fall -

102

ing,   and You've told   me who   I   am:____

I   am Yours._____   I   am Yours._

I   am Yours._____

━ **SCENE 7** ━

Characters: **Jacob** and **Miriam**

Setting: Both characters are standing in the shed.

JACOB: That's why I keep this staff around here, Miriam *(placing it back on the wall, hanging sideways, like it was at the beginning)*. It reminds me... of who I am...and who He is.

MIRIAM: But why do you keep it hanging like that? Sideways? Whenever I see a shepherd's staff somewhere, it's usually propped up against a wall, standing up.

JACOB: Well, I'll tell you *(sitting down on a hay bale in front of **Miriam**, holding both of her hands in his for a minute)*. Miriam, there's no way I could ever forget that night the angels appeared—the night I saw Baby Jesus in His mother's arms. That staff is special to me because it reminds me of that time, but...even without it...that night is never too far away in my memory.

But there was another night—actually, it was the middle of the afternoon, but it LOOKED like night—literally! It FELT like night—no sun—nothing but darkness. And there was Jesus—no longer a baby, but a grown man, all alone.

The angels weren't there this time. There was nothing happy about this occasion. I don't know if angels cry, but...I know old shepherds do because...I stood there...just a face in the crowd, but...I couldn't believe it. There He was! Nailed to a cross!

Whenever I'd seen Him before, I'd always been able to spot the resemblance to that tiny Baby I'd seen in the manger. I'd rub my chin, smile, and remember. But this time...it didn't look like Him, Miriam. In fact, He hardly looked like a man at all—torn and bruised and bloody.

MIRIAM: Why?

JACOB: Because He loved us—even people who didn't love Him back. Even people who never knew they needed a Savior...and if they DID know it...wouldn't have wanted one.

Jesus had said, "'The one who has seen Me has seen the Father'" (John 14:9). And when I saw Him that day, dying on the cross for my sins, I SAW the Father—a Father like me who knew what it was like to watch His Son die—a Father who cared for people like me, with little families like mine—and who would stop at nothing to show His love for me.

(standing, moving where the staff is hanging) So...that's why I keep it hanging sideways like this, so I'll never forget the time He stretched out His arms all day on another big hunk of wood to take away all my sins and give me a new reason to live.

MIRIAM: *(standing, going to **Jacob**)* Grandfather...I don't want to forget, either. But I wasn't there to see Him. How can I remember...the way you do?

JACOB: You don't have to see Jesus with your own eyes to remember how much He loves you. No matter who you are—or how old you are— you can still treasure Him in your heart, just like I do. How did He say it? *(trying to remember)* "Where your treasure is, there your heart will be also" (Matt. 6:21).

MIRIAM: Even for somebody like me?

JACOB: *(smiling through tears)* Oh, yes, Miriam,...He can be your treasure, too.

(pausing as an unexpected thought enters his mind) I tell you what *(taking the staff off the wall)*...why don't YOU take this? *(handing it to **Miriam**)* Why don't you take this and keep it as your own treasure? And then every time you look at it, you can remember how Jesus died for you and for me. And every time we come into this shed and see the empty place where it used to hang, we'll remember that He came down OFF that cross, and that He lives again—and that because His tomb is empty, one day we'll ALL get to be there when the angels announce His arrival.

And, oh, Miriam, *(placing his hands on her shoulders)* I don't want you to miss that! *(music begins)*

*(**Miriam** smiles up into **Jacob's** eyes, the love and admiration passing between them. The music starts as she slowly, lovingly carries the staff to front center stage and begins her song of praise and awe, visually including the audience in the tender experience.)*

What Can I Give Him?

with

Everything

Words and Music by MIKE HARLAND
Arranged by Camp Kirkland

Words based on "What Can I Give Him" by Christina G. Rossetti.

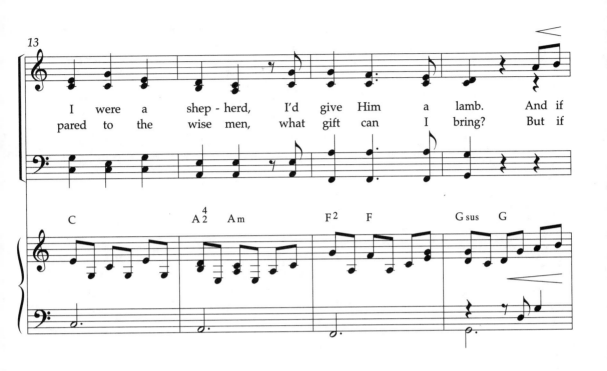

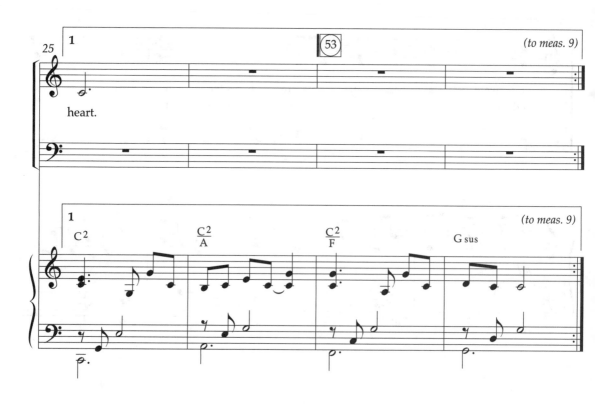

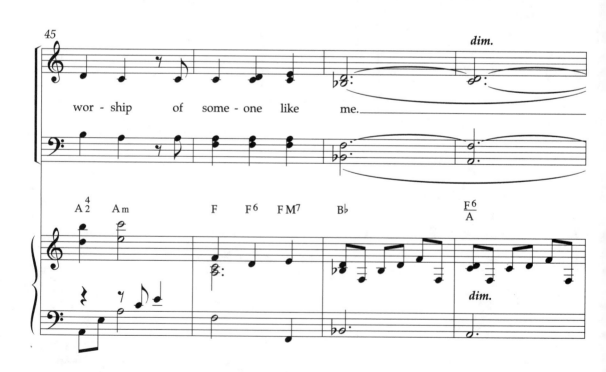

57

74
Ev - 'ry - thing,___ ev - 'ry - thing,___

Db   Ab/Db   Db/F   Fm7

76   *mf*
Lord, You___ are___ ev - 'ry - thing to___ me.___ My trea-

GbM7 Gb6   Gb   Gb/Ab   Ab7   Db

78
sure,___ my pri - or - i - ty.___

Ab   Db/Ab   Bbm7   Ebm/C   Db

mf

116

58

1st time

(CONGREGATION MAY JOIN)

~ SCENE 8 ~

Characters: **Jacob** and **Miriam**

Setting: Just as **Miriam** finishes her song, **Jacob** joins her onstage. This is their moment.

JACOB: I never dreamed, Miriam, that there could be anything as special as standing in the same stable with the baby Jesus. But now I know one thing that is…just as special—standing here with you, knowing that Jesus is right here with us.

And I never imagined I'd ever see anything so sweet as Mary, sitting there singing to her new Baby, treasuring every moment of His birth in her heart. But now I know one thing that's just as good—seeing my own little granddaughter treasuring that same Jesus in her heart. *(music begins)*

Yes, I've been there, Miriam. I've seen Him. I've seen Jesus. But He's as much yours now as He is mine. Isn't it wonderful? *(hugging her)*

MIRIAM: It really is.

JACOB: Yes, He really is.

Jesus, What a Wonder You Are
with
Fairest Lord Jesus

Words and Music by
MIKE HARLAND and **LUKE GARRETT**
Arranged by Camp Kirkland

61

search of some-thing more, and nev - er know the won-der___ that You

F2   B♭M7   Gm7   F/A   B♭2

CHOIR

are.   But noth-ing we have here will last for-

G2   B♭M7

ev-er;___ our trea-sures on-ly rise un-til they fall.

MEN

But

C2   B♭M7   Dm

† "Fairest Lord Jesus." Words Anonymous German Hymn, *Munster Gesangbuch*; st. 1, tr. source unknown; st. 4, JOSEPH AUGUSTUS SEISS. Music *Schlesische Volkslieder*, arr. Richard Storrs Willis.

130

SCENE 9

Characters: **Jacob** and **Miriam**

Setting: **Jacob** and **Miriam**, carrying the staff, are front center stage for a quick finale.

MIRIAM: *(holding the staff out to him) (music begins)* Where do you think I should keep it, Grandfather?

JACOB: Oh, Miriam, you don't really KEEP Jesus anywhere. You just go share Him. Just…go, tell everybody!

FINALE
includes
Go, Tell Everybody
with
Go, Tell It on the Mountain
and
Jesus, Our Treasure

we have heard___ and we have seen.

† "Go, Tell It on the Mountain"

Go, tell it on the moun - tain,___ O - ver the hills and

† "Go, Tell It on the Mountain." Words by JOHN W. WORK, JR. Music: African-American Spiritual.

17
ev - 'ry - where; Go, tell it on the moun - tain That
A♭ D♭/E♭ A♭ B♭m7 A♭/C B♭9
72
20
ff
Je - sus Christ is born! I said,
B♭m7 D♭M7/E♭ E♭7 D♭ A♭ E♭/F F

go, tell ev-'ry-bod-y what we have heard___ and we have

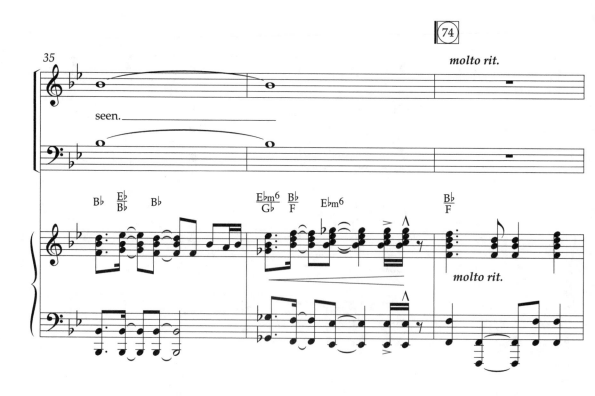

seen.___

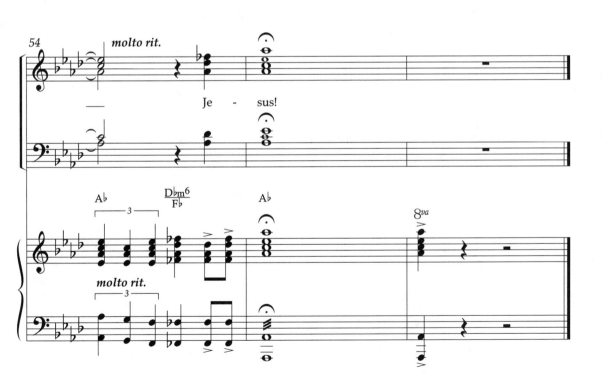

Production Suggestions

by Mike Harland

CHARACTERS
(in order of appearance)

MIRIAM: Young girl, about 10, Jacob's granddaughter; speaking and singing role; appears in every scene, except Scene 3

JACOB: Man in his 60s, 40 years after the angel appeared to him as a shepherd; speaking and singing role; appears in every scene, except Scene 3; delivers the largest portion of dialogue; solo should be acted more than sung

ANGELS*: Acting role; appear in Scenes 2 and 3; use as many or as few as desired

SHEPHERDS: Any number of shepherds, from 3 to 10; acting and speaking role, with lines limited to one scene

YOUNG JACOB: One of the shepherds; acting and speaking role; It would be an added bonus if the actor's physical characteristics reflect the older Jacob's appearance.

MARY: Acting and singing role; sings "My Son, My Lord"; appears in Scenes 3 and 5

JOSEPH: Acting and singing role; sings "My Son, My Lord"; appears in Scenes 3 and 5

BABY JESUS*: Crying and cooing role; appears in "My Son, My Lord" and Scene 3

BOY JESUS*: A young-looking 4-year-old or mature 3-year-old; acting role. Use your judgment.

WISE MEN*: At least three wise men, but there could be more. Each wise man can have any number of attendants, from none to six or seven.

HEROD: Man in his late 60s, early 70s; acting and singing role; challenging role requiring a confident actor and singer

*optional characters

Sets and Props

JACOB'S SHED

All dialogue happens in this set. It does not have to be big but should have plenty of "stuff," including items **Miriam** mentions in Scene 1 (sickle, multicolored robe, small wood-carved sheep, and, most importantly, **Jacob's** old staff hanging horizontally). Provide seating for **Jacob** and **Miriam** to allow different staging options during scenes.

MANGER

This set is featured during the **Mary/Joseph** duet, "My Son, My Lord." It should be large enough to allow **Mary** and **Joseph** to have their own "space" during their verses and to come together on the duet, as well as large enough for the shepherds to join them during "What Child Is This."

HEROD'S COURT

This set is featured during "Herod's Song." If it cannot be a permanent fixture throughout the musical, the effect can be achieved with easily movable props, such as portico/balcony pieces, a regal chair, or additional characters in costume accompanying **Herod** with handheld props and accessories.

HOUSE IN BETHLEHEM

The **wise men** meet the **boy Jesus** here, along with **Mary** and **Joseph**. It should be centrally located and would work best if it could be moved into place just before the scene. A small table with crude carpentry tools and sturdy wood for the boy to stand on would work well as the centerpiece.

LIGHTS AND SOUND

Stage lighting is an important part of this production. Preset area production lights mounted on lighting trees (which can be rented from most production companies) or lights mounted on permanent trusses add realism. "Source lighting" is also effective. For example, a candle or lamp burning in the shed adds depth and dimension. Soloists can be highlighted with follow spots and stage lights. Follow spots can also mark the shepherds and wise men's path. Use all available lighting options to enhance the moods and moments throughout the production. Select brighter settings for moments of joy and celebration; select dimmer lighting for tender moments of reflection. Variety holds the audience's attention as the story progresses.

Having adequate monitors placed across the sets is very important, whether using live or recorded accompaniment. Plan for this when considering where each set will be and the number of outputs located in each area.

Wireless lapel or headset microphones are preferred for **Jacob** and **Miriam**. Soloists that sing in character (**Mary**, **Joseph**, **Herod**) should also use lapel or headset microphones if the microphones produce "singing quality." They may be purchased or rented from most sound equipment suppliers. These microphones add to the characters' effectiveness. However, if a handheld microphone is your best option, that is fine. I always think "sound effect" before I think "visual effect."

The trio featured in "Jesus, Our Treasure" can use handheld microphones since they do not sing in character.

SONG BY SONG
AND
SCENE BY SCENE SUGGESTIONS

LET THERE BE JOY with JOY TO THE WORLD! THE LORD IS COME and HOW GREAT OUR JOY

This is an energetic call to worship featuring the choir. Add energy with a six- to nine-voice vocal team, or allow the vocal team to present the entire song as the choir processes into the sanctuary.

INTERLUDE 1 (JESUS, OUR TREASURE)

This short interlude introduces the theme song in a slower, blended style. As it begins, bring lights up on **Miriam** in **Jacob's** shed. She begins looking around the shed as the interlude concludes.

SCENE 1

The scene begins immediately as the song ends. **Miriam** takes a moment with each prop she mentions. If you do not have a sickle, substitute another tool for that line.

GLORY TO GOD

A bright light should be on the **shepherds** and **angel**. As the choir begins, have the **shepherds** react to the **angel** (now joined by as many **angels** as desired). As the song ends, the **shepherds** should be outside the "door" of the manger, looking in, but not disturbing this intimate moment.

SCENE 2

Joseph interacts with the **shepherds** as **Mary** shares this moment with her Baby. **Jacob's** shed fades to black as the dialogue concludes, and the focus shifts to the manger for the duet. If Mary sings the chorus in the key of B♭, it will set up the intro of the duet.

MY SON, MY LORD with WHAT CHILD IS THIS

Mary and **Joseph** are on separate sides of the manger set for stanza 1. It would be effective if **Mary** could hold **Baby Jesus** while she sings stanza 1, then hand him to **Joseph** to hold as he sings stanza 2. They should come together as they sing the duet.
It will take a cooperative baby to pull this off. Their focus should be on the baby as they sing, whether or not they hold him.

SCENE 3

The written dialogue could be ad libbed with similar lines.

GO, TELL EVERYBODY with GO, TELL IT ON THE MOUNTAIN

Ask the congregation to sing along on "Go, Tell It on the Mountain."

SCENE 4

This scene contains some of the most important information of the presentation. Do not rush this dialogue!

HEROD'S SONG (I AM THE KING)

This song requires a good singer and an even better actor. Ensure that the line "no more than two" is emphasized in stanza 2. A dark, even haunting sound from the men's section during the second refrain as they sing "O Come, O Come, Emmanuel" will add to the tension.

INTERLUDE 2 (O COME, O COME, EMMANUEL)

Nothing happens here. Allow the audience to digest the previous scene.

SCENE 5

The dialogue is critical. Slow it down. Let the audience absorb every word.

JESUS, OUR TREASURE

The men's trio is away from the main set but visible and part of the moment. If **wise men** are used, every second of the song will be needed to present a processional complete with elaborate costumes, extravagant gifts, and attendants. They process to center stage and are met by **Mary**, **Joseph**, and the **boy Jesus**. Jesus would have been two or under, but I recommend a small four-year-old or mature, cooperative three-year-old. Using a boy for this scene communicates an often-missed aspect of the story: significant time passed before the **wise men** came—it could have been months, or even two years. The entire cast should bow at the end of the song and hold their position to enhance this worship moment.

INTERLUDE 3 (JESUS, OUR TREASURE)

If you fully stage a **wise men's** processional during "Jesus, Our Treasure," this interlude provides the pause needed to clear the stage and continue the flow of the musical. If a processional is not included, the interlude could be played as a transition or omitted.

SCENE 6

A short pause may be needed to allow time for the cast to exit from the previous scene. **Jacob** transitions right into the song.

WHO AM I?

Jacob could present this powerful song at center stage. He should not overdo the solo to avoid diminishing his portrayal of a shepherd until this point. Direct him to present the song like the character would present it. Great singing is not to be the focus, as demonstrated effectively on the recording. As he finishes, he slowly returns to the shed with **Miriam**.

SCENE 7

To set up this scene, the staff has been a visible and important prop throughout the presentation. Now **Jacob** takes it and lovingly presents it to **Miriam**. Again, it is important not to rush the dialogue. Let every word soak in. **Miriam** moves immediately into her solo and holds the staff throughout the song.

WHAT CAN I GIVE HIM? with EVERYTHING

Miriam can move out of the set to sing her solo. After the choir begins singing, she can return to the set and interact with **Jacob**. As the end of the song draws near, she can sing the last line of the song. Then **Jacob** gives her a grandfatherly hug. The congregation can join in singing "Everything." Consider singing this song several times in worship before the performance so the congregation will be able to sing it confidently.

SCENE 8

This is short but full of warmth—lots of hugs and smiles.

JESUS, WHAT A WONDER YOU ARE with FAIREST LORD JESUS

Let the song say it all!

INVITATION

This would be an excellent place for the pastor or other minister to give the opportunity for the audience to respond to the presentation. My prayer is that people will have the joy of welcoming new Christians into the kingdom of the Lord wherever this story is presented. Consider using the chorus "Everything" from "What Can I Give Him" or the refrain of "Jesus, What a Wonder You Are" as an invitation song.

SCENE 9

Jacob and **Miriam** are excited as they present these last two lines. Bring the entire cast (except **Herod** and the **baby Jesus**) back out and have them sing along. On the last "Jesus," the entire cast should kneel, and **Miriam** should hold the staff horizontally above her head. Hold this pose until the audience responds. Let it soar!

FINALE includes GO, TELL EVERYBODY with GO, TELL IT ON THE MOUNTAIN and JESUS, OUR TREASURE

Invite the congregation to sing along!